Literature

and the Language Arts

Experiencing Literature

APPLIED ENGLISH

THE EMC MASTERPIECE SERIES

EMCParadigm Publishing Saint Paul, Minnesota

Staff Credits

Editorial

Laurie Skiba
Editor

Brenda Owens
Associate Editor

Lori Ann Coleman
Associate Editor

Diana Moen
Associate Editor

Gia Marie Garbinsky
Assistant Editor

Jennifer Joline Anderson
Assistant Editor

Janice Johnson
Curriculum Specialist

Paul Spencer
Art and Photo Researcher

Chris Bohen
Editorial Assistant

Chris Nelson
Editorial Assistant

Katherine S. Link
Editorial Assistant

Design

Shelley Clubb
Production Manager

C. Vern Johnson
Senior Designer

Cover Credits

Cover Designer: C. Vern Johnson

Gas [Detail], 1940. Edward Hopper.

Last of the Buffalo [Detail], 1889. Albet Bierstadt.

His Hammer in His Hand [Detail], from the John Henry Series, 1944–7. Palmer Hayden.

ISBN 0-8219-2116-9
© 2001 EMC Corporation

Published by EMC/Paradigm Publishing
875 Montreal Way
St. Paul, Minnesota 55102
800-328-1452
www.emcp.com
E-mail: educate@emcp.com

Printed in the United States of America.
10 9 8 7 6 5 4 3 2   XXX   03 04 05 06 07 08 09

Contents

Applied English Resource

6.1 FILLING OUT FORMS

Filling out forms is something you will do on many occasions throughout your life. On a form you provide requested information about yourself. To do this in a way that makes a good impression, keep the following guidelines in mind.

- Read through the directions and the form itself before writing anything.
- Complete the form neatly. Avoid smudges and cross-outs. Use the writing method requested, such using black or blue ink.
- Do not leave any lines blank. If an item does not apply to you, write N.A. for "not applicable."
- Proofread for accuracy and for errors in punctuation, spelling, and grammar.

EXERCISES

A. Completing a Volunteer Information Form

Fill out the volunteer information form following the guidelines above.

VOLUNTEER INFORMATION
BELMONT COMMUNITY YOUTH SOCCER ASSOCIATION

Name _____

Address _____

Phone _____ Best time to call _____ E-mail _____

The Belmont Community Youth Soccer Association operates from 9 a.m. to 3 p.m. on Saturdays, from 1 p.m. to 5 p.m. Sundays, and from 6 p.m. until 9 p.m. on selected weekdays. Volunteers are asked to volunteer for a 2-hour or 4-hour shift at least once a week.

Preferred duties: _____

Number of hours you wish to work per month: _____

Length of shift: _____

Preferred day(s): _____

Preferred time of day: _____

Have you ever worked in a soccer program or other children's sports program before? If yes, please explain what you did there.

_____

_____

_____

A volunteer coordinator will contact you. Thank you for your interest!

B. Completing a Grant Application Form

Imagine that you want to apply for a grant from a local community organization to pay for a traffic safety project at an elementary school in your school district. Meet with several other students to come up with a possible project. Estimate the materials you will need and their cost. Then, work together to complete the grant application form below.

COMMUNITY FOUNDATION

Application Form for Grant Programs

Use this form if you are applying for a mini-grant of $500 or less. All projects must benefit, enhance, or improve student life.

Do not write in this space!

FY _____ APP # _____ RAT _____ AMT _____

School name/address: _____

_____

_____

Phone: _____ /_____

Student project leader: _____

Other student participants: _____

Advisor: _____

Describe your project in the space below (attach sketch if needed): _____

_____

_____

How will this project enhance your school district and its students? _____

_____

_____

Materials needed for project: _____

Estimated cost of materials: _____

Estimated time to complete project: _____

I hereby certify that all statements on this application are true and correct to the best of my knowledge. Submission of this application signifies intention of compliance with all general and specific guidelines of the Community Foundation.

_____   _____
Signature   Date of application

6.2 FOLLOWING DIRECTIONS

Being able to follow spoken and written directions is an essential skill, both in the classroom and on the job. Here are some guidelines for following directions.

- If the directions are spoken, take notes as you listen. Ask for clarification if needed.
- If the directions are written, read through them before beginning.
- If written directions include words you don't know, look them up or check for definitions in the attached materials.
- If you get stuck, retrace your steps or reread the step you are on. Consult diagrams or illustrations if available.

EXERCISES

A. Following Written Directions

Read the following directions, which describe how to measure your cardiorespiratory endurance, and study the diagram. Follow the directions to measure your general physical flexibility. Then answer the questions.

To take this test, you will need a partner and a wooden or cardboard box. Sit on the floor with your legs straight and your feet flat against the box. Lean forward at the waist and stretch your arms toward the box as far as you can. Hold this position for five seconds. Have your partner measure the distance you can reach. Reaching the exact edge of the box means a measurement of 0. If you cannot reach the box, your measurement will be negative (-1 inch, -2 inches, etc.). If you can reach past the edge of the box, your measurement will be positive (1 inch, 2 inches, etc.)

For girls, the degree of flexibility is good if the score is +2 to +4 inches, fair if +2 to -1, and poor if -2 to -4. For boys, the degree of flexibility is good if the score is +1 to +3 inches, fair if +1 to -3, and poor if -3 to -6.

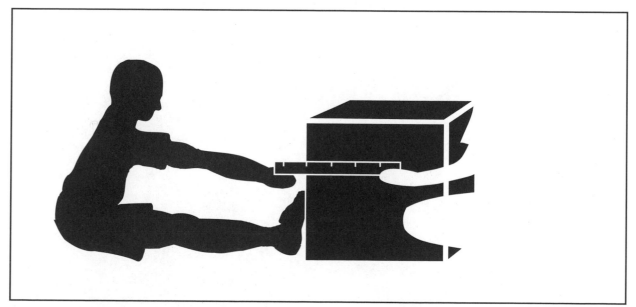

1. Why do you need a partner to take this test?

_____

2. What information did you get from the diagram that was not given in the directions?

_____

B. Following Spoken Directions

In a listing of television programs, find an instructional program such as a cooking, computer, painting, or home repair show. Watch the show. Then, on the lines below, write down in your own words the instructions given for a particular task.

_____

_____

_____

_____

_____

6.3 Giving Directions

No matter what kind of job you hold, you will often need to give directions to another person. The guidelines below will help ensure that the directions you give are clear and easy to follow.

- Think through the directions from start to finish before you begin.
- Give the steps in a logical order.
- Include all necessary steps. Unless you are very sure, do not assume your listener or reader already knows any part of the task.
- Use simple and precise language.
- Use transition words, such as *first, second, third, next, then,* and *finally.*
- Use a similar sentence structure for each part of the directions when possible.
- When giving directions orally, ask the listener to repeat the directions to you when you have finished.
- Include a map, diagram, or other illustration when it would be useful.

EXERCISES

A. Giving Directions Orally

Assume you are speaking on the phone to an out-of-town relative staying at your house who is coming to pick you up at school. This relative needs directions for getting to your school. In your directions, include landmarks to watch for, road names, and turns as well as where to park and enter the school. Consult a map and make notes if you need to. Have a partner listen to your oral directions to confirm that they are clear and accurate.

Notes for oral directions

_____

_____

_____

_____

_____

_____

_____

Questions or comments from listener

_____

_____

_____

_____

_____

_____

_____

B. Giving Directions in Writing

Rewrite the following instructions to make them clearer, using the guidelines above.

Directions for Doing a Load of Laundry

Pour the detergent into the washing bin. But don't forget to measure it first. Then start the machine. But first choose the correct settings on the washer for your laundry load. Then lay the clothes in loosely, filling the washer about 2/3 full. However, wait about 15 seconds after you start the washing machine before putting in the clothes to make sure the detergent is dissolved or spread evenly around the bin. Your clothes should be sorted into white and colored articles before you start to do the laundry. Close the lid. Then either hang up the clothes to dry or put them in the dryer. Be sure to take clothes out of the dryer as soon as the machine has finished its cycle. Also, when the washing load is finished, take out the clothes immediately to avoid wrinkling.

_____

_____

_____

_____

_____

_____

_____

_____

_____

_____

_____

_____

_____

_____

_____

_____

_____

_____

_____

6.4   WRITING A STEP-BY-STEP PROCEDURE

Preparing a step-by-step procedure is useful when you need to teach someone a new process. A written procedure includes numbered steps and sometimes graphics. A spoken procedure can include an actual demonstration of the process. In addition to following the guidelines for "Giving Directions" (see activity 6.3), keep these points in mind when writing or demonstrating a step-by-step procedure.

- If you are showing how to make something, create samples to show the different steps. You could also include examples of variations on the final product.
- Think about what it would be like to be learning the procedure for the first time. Try to anticipate problems and be prepared for them. See if you can follow your own directions, or have a friend work through them and offer suggestions.
- Know your topic well. If something goes wrong when you are giving a live demonstration, be prepared to explain why. The audience can learn from your mistakes.

EXERCISES

A. Showing a Step-by-Step Procedure

Assume you are in charge of a team of students who have volunteered to teach bicycle safety to a group of young children. The presentation includes a review of traffic laws, a description of safe-riding guidelines, and a demonstration on how to use safety equipment. On the lines below, gives some tips for presenting the step-by-step procedure of how to apply reflective safety tape to helmets, shoes, and bicycles. Then write the procedure for applying reflective tape to a bicycle.

Tips

_____

_____

_____

_____

_____

Procedure for applying reflective tape to a bicycle

_____

_____

_____

_____

_____

B. Writing a Step-by-Step Procedure

Using the guidelines above, along with those in activity 6.3, write a step-by-step procedure for each of the following.

1. Cleaning or repairing something (such as washing a window or untangling a cassette tape)

_____

_____

_____

_____

_____

_____

2. Making something (such as a favorite food or an article of clothing)

_____

_____

_____

_____

_____

_____

3. Doing an important procedure in a sport or game

_____

_____

_____

_____

_____

_____

6.5 WRITING A BUSINESS LETTER

To make a good impression in a business letter, you should use a formal tone, follow the correct form, and avoid errors in spelling, grammar, usage, and mechanics. Business letters are often typed in **block form**, in which each part of the letter begins at the left margin and the parts are separated by a blank line. A business letter should include

- an inside address, including the recipient's name and title and the company (or organization) name and address
- a salutation that begins with the word *Dear*, followed by the courtesy or professional title used in the inside address, such as Ms. Mr., or Dr., and a colon
- the body, in which you make your points clearly in as few words as possible
- a standard closing such as *Sincerely*, or *Yours truly*
- your signature, in blue or black ink

EXERCISES

A. Writing a Business Letter

Everyone has an ideal summer job. What's yours? Write a short business letter requesting that you be considered for your ideal summer job. Explain why you are interested in the job, as well as why you feel you are qualified. Request an interview. Use the lines below to make notes about whom you will write to and the main points you will make. Then, on a separate sheet of paper, write your letter, following the guidelines above and the model on page 1054 of your textbook. If you cannot word-process your letter, print it neatly on lined paper.

_____

_____

_____

_____

_____

_____

_____

_____

_____

_____

_____

_____

_____

_____

_____

_____

_____

_____

B. Conduct a Letter-Writing Campaign

Through letter-writing campaigns, citizens can influence decision makers on important issues. Issue-related letters are often addressed to one or more public officials. Choose an issue or cause that is important to you and write a letter supporting that cause to an appropriate public official.

6.6   WRITING A MEMO

Within a business or organization, people often use **memos** to communicate information, announcements, and instructions. The word *memo* is short for *memorandum* (plural *memoranda*). A memo written to someone you know well or for a social purpose, such as announcing a party, may be informal in tone. However, most memos have a fairly formal tone. A memo begins with a header followed by the names of the sender and recipient, the subject (*RE:* means "regarding"), and date.

SAMPLE MEMO

Memorandum

TO: Lucy Hinkens
FR: Damar Jones
RE: Shakespeare performance
DT: March 6, 2000

Please let all of the students in your drama classes know that the Reduced Shakespeare Company will be giving an afternoon performance on Sunday, April 20, at 3 p.m. at Memorial Auditorium. The ensemble is known for their condensed and humorous presentations of Shakespeare's plays. The cost is $4 per student with ID.

Thank you.

EXERCISES

A. Writing a Business Memo

Imagine that you are the secretary of the Outdoor Club at your school. The club plans hikes, ski trips, canoe trips, and other outdoor events throughout the school year. A canoe trip is planned for next month, and it is your duty to announce it. The trip will take place on Saturday, May 3 on the Mohican River near Clear Fork. Canoes can be rented from the Mohican Canoe Rental Company at a discounted cost of $25 per canoe for a half day, including paddles and floatation vests. A bus will leave the school parking lot at 7 a.m. and return at 3 p.m. Students should bring a sack lunch and drink. Snacks will be provided. All students participating will need to obtain a permission form from you, have it signed by a parent or guardian, and bring it with them on May 3. Interested students can obtain more information from you or any Outdoor Club officer. Write a memo to "All Members" of the club announcing the canoe trip.

TO: _____

FR: _____

RE: _____

DT: _____

_____

_____

_____

_____

_____

_____

_____

B. Memo Writing

Imagine that you are a movie producer and have decided to make a film based on Gabriel García Marquez's short story, "The Handsomest Drowned Man in the World" (pages 216-23 in your textbook). You need to find financial backing to make the film. Write a memo to Ms. Rhoda de la Riche, a wealthy individual who invests her money in films. Explain why you feel the story would make a good film and why you are qualified to make it. Include any other information you think would help Ms. de la Riche decide to back your project.

TO: _____

FR: _____

RE: _____

DT: _____

_____

_____

_____

_____

_____

_____

_____

_____

_____

_____

_____

_____

_____

_____

_____

_____

_____

_____

_____

_____

_____

_____

_____

_____

6.7   WRITING A PROPOSAL

A **proposal** outlines a project that a person or group wants to complete. It presents a summary of the project, the reasons why the project is important, and an outline of how the project would be carried out. A proposal should be both informative and persuasive. The following tips can help you create an effective proposal.

- Use a positive, courteous tone and standard, formal English.
- Use headings, lists, and schedules to make the proposal easy to review.
- State your purpose and rationale clearly and briefly.
- Include all necessary information; try to anticipate and answer any questions reviewers might have.

EXERCISES

A. Making Notes for a Proposal

Imagine that you are organizing a Volunteer Day at your school. To think about how you might organize your proposal, review the elements of a proposal and read the sample on pages 1055-56 of your textbook. Then answer the questions that follow.

1. Which of the following purpose statements for your project is more effective and why?

   Proposal: To have a Volunteer Day.

   Proposal: To organize a Volunteer Day to inform students about volunteer opportunities in the community and emphasize the many benefits of volunteering

   _____

   _____

   _____

   _____

   _____

2. Write a possible rationale for this proposal.

   _____

   _____

   _____

   _____

3. What possible headings could you use for the sections explaining how the project would be carried out?

   _____

   _____

   _____

   _____

   _____

B. Writing a Proposal

Referring to the notes you made above and the sample proposal on page 1056 of your textbook, write a proposal for the school Volunteer Day on the lines below.

Proposal: _____

_____

Rationale: _____

_____

_____

_____

_____

Schedule / Preparation Outline: _____

_____

_____

_____

_____

_____

_____

_____

Needs and Estimated Costs: _____

_____

_____

_____

_____

_____

_____

Estimated Income: _____

_____

_____

_____

_____

6.8 WRITING A RÉSUMÉ

An effective résumé can help you obtain the job, volunteer opportunity, or other position you want. A **résumé** is a summary of your career objectives, previous employment experience, and education. Here are a few key guidelines for writing a résumé.

- Keep your information to one page if possible.
- Place vital contact information (name, address, phone number) at the top.
- Use short headings to organize the information. When you list your volunteer or work experience, start with the most recent position.
- Be honest and accurate in giving information, but emphasize the positive.
- Type your résumé on white or cream-colored paper and proofread it carefully.
- List references or state that they are available upon request.

EXERCISES

A. Writing a Résumé

Take a moment to consider the types of jobs or volunteer opportunities that might fit your current skills, interests, and experience. On the lines below, describe your objective, educational background, and work or other experience as you would on a résumé. If you have not held a paying job yet, list volunteer experiences or relevant school projects. Use the information and sample résumé on page 1057 of your textbook as a guide.

Objective

_____

_____

_____

Education

_____

_____

_____

_____

_____

_____

Work Experience

_____

_____

_____

_____

_____

_____

B. Writing a Cover Letter for Your Résumé

When you send your résumé to a possible employer, volunteer coordinator, or other person, you should also send a cover letter. This letter explains your interest in a particular position and briefly states why you are qualified for it. The qualifications you mention should be reflected in your résumé. In your cover letter you should also request an interview and state the best time for contacting you. Cover letters should follow the guidelines you learned for writing business letters in activity 6.5.

Assume that you are applying for a part-time job or volunteer position that fits some of your interests and skills. Write a cover letter to accompany your résumé.

_____

_____

_____

_____

_____

_____

_____

_____

_____

_____

_____

_____

_____

_____

_____

_____

_____

_____

_____

_____

_____

_____

_____

_____

_____

6.9 DELIVERING A PRESS RELEASE

A **press release** is a brief promotional piece often used to announce an upcoming event. A press release is intended for distribution through a news outlet, such as a radio station or local newspaper.

SAMPLE NEWS RELEASE

For release: Immediately   Columbus Outdoor Pursuits
Contact person: Barb Sharp   614/447-1006
March 3, 2000

The 39th annual Tour of the Scioto River Valley takes place May 13 and 14 this year. Each year this scenic tour draws thousands of bicyclists of all ages from across the Midwest and beyond. The two-day round trip from Columbus to Portsmouth follows country roads along the Scioto River, passing through the hills, farmland, and small towns of southern Ohio. Cyclists assemble on the State House lawn for an early take-off Saturday morning and most return late Sunday afternoon. The total length of the tour is 210 miles. The registration fee is $33. Overnight accommodations and meals in Portsmouth may be arranged at extra cost. Registration forms and more information can be obtained at the TOSRV website: www.tosrv.org.

EXERCISES

A. Writing a Press Release

Write a press release announcing an upcoming event at your school or in your community. Alternatively, you may wish to invent an event, such as the opening of an animal shelter, a Fourth of July celebration, or tryouts for a school play.

For Immediate Release: _____ Contact: _____

Date: _____

From (place name): _____

Headline: _____

_____

_____

_____

_____

_____

_____

_____

_____

_____

_____

_____

B. Writing a Press Release

A press release should capture a reader's attention and persuade the reader to feel positive about a particular event. Imagine that you're in charge of public relations for a theater company. The company's next performance will be of William Shakespeare's *Romeo and Juliet*. Write a press release to persuade the public to attend the performance. Before you write, review the background on Shakespeare and his play on pages 298-99 of your textbook. Include the following information in your press release:

Date of press release
Contact person
Dates and times of the performances
Location
Background about the play and author
Names of the leading actors
Cost of tickets
How to purchase tickets

Why people should attend

_____

_____

_____

_____

_____

_____

_____

_____

_____

_____

_____

_____

_____

_____

_____

_____

_____

_____

_____

_____

_____

_____

6.10 WRITING A PUBLIC SERVICE ANNOUNCEMENT

A **public service announcement,** or PSA, is a brief, informative article intended to be helpful to the community. Most PSAs are written by nonprofit organizations. For example, your county health department might issue a PSA in the fall telling people about the benefits of flu shots and where to get one. The PSA is similar in format to a press release (see activity 6.9). Keep these points in mind when writing a PSA.

- State the information objectively and briefly.
- Tell your audience *who, what, where, when,* and *how.*
- Place the most important information at the beginning of your story.
- Include contact information at the top and the word "END" at the bottom.

EXERCISES

A. Writing a Public Service Announcement

Review the discussion of PSAs on page 1058 of your textbook. Write a public service announcement to promote Diabetes Awareness Week. The event is sponsored by your local health department and will be broadcast on the radio. The purpose of the PSA is to increase people's awareness of the disease diabetes. You may wish to do some research on diabetes before writing your PSA.

Organization or cause:

_____

Message to communicate:

_____

_____

Effect you wish to have on your audience (i.e., how you want your audience to think or act after hearing your message):

_____

_____

Way to grab audience attention at beginning of message:

_____

_____

Sound effects to be used:

_____

Number of voices and characters, and description of each:

_____

_____

B. Writing a Public Service Announcement

Select a topic for a public service announcement that would benefit people in your community. Some possible ideas are announcements to encourage people to drive safely, recycle, exercise regularly, read to their children, or have their blood pressure checked. Check the library or the Internet if you need to do more research on your topic before writing. Write a brief PSA for the topic you chose.

6.11 DISPLAYING EFFECTIVE VISUAL INFORMATION

Using visuals—such as photographs, slides, pictures, models, charts, or tables—can enhance almost any presentation. Visuals focus and hold audience attention and help people grasp facts and concepts quickly. You can also use visuals to clarify a complex procedure, show comparisons, or emphasize key points.

GUIDELINES FOR USING VISUALS

- Always use visuals of high quality.
- Make sure each visual serves a real purpose.
- Keep visuals simple, neat, and uncluttered.
- Clearly label your visual display. Include a title, captions, and labels.
- Make sure all visuals and text are large enough to see or read.
- Use bullets or numbering to organize visual displays of text.
- Use color carefully; too much color can be distracting.
- Document all sources of graphic information.

EXERCISES

A. Selecting and Evaluating Ideas for Visuals

Choosing the right visuals can make all the difference between a great presentation and one that seems ho-hum. Review the discussion of effective visuals on page 1059 of your textbook. Then, in the first space on the chart on this page, describe a presentation you'd like to make about one of the authors featured in your textbook. Use the rest of the chart to list and evaluate possible types of visual information to include in your presentation. You might want to consider photos, maps, posters, or other types of visuals.

Subject of presentation _____

_____

Type of Visual	Reasons for Using	Possible Drawbacks

B. Creating an Effective Visual

Imagine that you have been asked to create a music video or CD cover art for a song. The text of the song is one of the poems in Unit 2 of your book (pages 74-161) or one from Part 2 (pages 564-947) that represents a particular theme. Review the poems, choosing one that especially appeals to you. Then, in the space below, make notes and a thumbnail sketch of a key scene from the video or the CD cover art. Consider how the text and graphics will work together to express the song's meaning. Before you begin, you may want to review "Preparing a Multimedia Presentation" on page 1029 of your textbook.

_____

_____

_____

_____

_____

_____

_____

_____

_____

6.12 WORKING ON A TEAM

Both in school and on the job, many of the tasks you do will require collaborating with others. Developing the following skills can help you to be an effective team member.

- Clarify what role or task each member of the team will take.
- Try to take on constructive roles and avoid destructive roles.
- Take responsibility for your share of the work.
- In discussions, make comments and ask questions at appropriate times.
- Listen attentively to other members of the team.
- Critically evaluate decisions and ideas, and speak out if you disagree.
- Stay focused on the issue or task at hand.
- Be polite, encouraging, and supportive.

EXERCISES

A. Taking Part in Team Discussions

Write what you could say in each of the following team situations to make a productive contribution.

1. Rex: How do you guys think we can get more kids involved in the traffic school? We could use 10 or 15 more volunteers. That way we wouldn't get so burned out from doing all the work. Do you think setting up a booth outside the cafeteria would be a good idea?

   Jonathan: Sure it would, as long as we paid each kid 50 bucks to volunteer.

   Shonté: If you don't think that's a good idea, Jonathan, just say so. You don't have to be sarcastic.

   Jonathan: I just don't think people will pay any attention to a stupid little booth.

   Felipe: I think it depends on how we present the message. We should try to make the booth funny and creative, so it will catch people's eyes.

   Denise: We could use music.

   Ben: And we could have some props, stuff we use at the traffic school.

   YOU: _____

   _____

2. Fran: We need to come up with some suggestions for our panel discussion in history class.

   Jordan: Why don't we start by making a list of possible subjects and ways we might approach them.

   Thomas: How'd you guys do on the history quiz? I think I aced it!

   YOU: _____

   _____

B. Collaborative Learning

Working in a small group, come up with a project on the topic "The Search for Self as Reflected in Literature." Assign a group leader to conduct the meetings of your project group. Then, all together, discuss the type of project you want to work on and how it might be organized. For example, will the end product be a poetry or fiction reading, a printed or audio anthology, a written or oral report, a multimedia presentation, or something else? Make an assignment sheet and assign tasks to specific group members. Develop a schedule for completing tasks and set times for future meetings to discuss progress and refine your ideas. On the lines below, make notes to help prepare for your group brainstorming and discussion.

1. Ideas for projects:

_____

_____

_____

2. How project might be organized:

_____

_____

_____

3. Poems and authors that might be included (see your textbook for some examples):

_____

_____

_____

4. Type of work I would most like to do:

_____

_____

_____

5. Type of work I would be willing to do:

_____

_____

_____

6. Things that group members can do to ensure the success of the project:

_____

_____

_____

Supplemental
Activity
Worksheets

English in Career Development

UNDERSTANDING TECHNICAL CAREERS

Choose one of the following technical careers or another technical career that interests you and research information about it. Then complete the following sheet based on the information that you gather.

SOME TECHNICAL CAREERS:

    word processing/data entry clerk

    computer programmer

    computer technician

    web master

    web page designer

    network administrator

    technical writer

    software engineer

    computer support technician

1. Career:_____

2. Training: _____

3. Typical Pay:_____

4. Benefits:_____

5. Working Conditions: _____

6. Amount of Social Interaction: _____

7. Positive Aspects of Job:_____

_____

8. Negative Aspects of Job: _____

_____

Why I would or would not like to work in this career:

_____

_____

_____

_____

INTERVIEW QUESTIONS

Imagine you are holding interviews for a position at the convenience store you manage. Use this space to plan your questions for your interview and to write down your applicant's responses. A few questions have been written for you to help you begin your interview. Begin your questions with the words *who, what, where, when, why* and *how*. Have a classmate answer the questions in your interview.

Where were you last employed?

_____

_____

How long did you work there?

_____

_____

Why did you leave this position?

_____

_____

What experience do you have with retail work?

_____

_____

_____

_____

_____

_____

_____

_____

_____

_____

_____

_____

_____

_____

_____

WRITING A RECOMMENDATION

Complete the following recommendation form for somebody you know. Imagine that he or she is applying for a job for which he or she is well suited.

Recommendation

Name of Applicant _____

Position Applied For _____

Recommended By _____

Address _____

Relationship to Applicant _____

Applicant is (please circle one)

Responsible	1	2	3	4	5
Hard-working	1	2	3	4	5
Mature	1	2	3	4	5
Honest	1	2	3	4	5
Punctual	1	2	3	4	5
	least				most

What special skills does the applicant bring to the position?

_____

_____

_____

In what ways has the applicant grown or changed in the time you have known him/her?

_____

_____

_____

What else would you like us to know about the applicant?

_____

_____

_____

English in Business

CREATING AN AGENDA

Imagine that you a member of Friends of the Everglades, the organization that published the article "For the Future of Florida: Repair the Everglades!" on page 517 in your textbook. A proposal has been put forward to build a jetport in Big Cypress Swamp, just west of the Everglades. Hold a meeting to discuss actions to stop the jetport and come up with a plan to preserve the Everglades. Complete the form below to create an agenda for your meeting.

AGENDA

Call Meeting to Order

Present Reason for Meeting: _____

Present Specific Problems Faced by Building of Jetport: _____

_____

_____

_____

_____

_____

_____

_____

_____

_____

Discussion of Possible Causes: _____

_____

_____

_____

_____

Discussion of Possible Solutions: _____

_____

_____

_____

_____

Adjourn Meeting

Project Report

Imagine that you are in charge of collecting provisions for your local food shelf. You have been asked to report on your progress in meeting your goals by the sponsors of the food shelf. Fill out the project report below.

PROJECT REPORT

TO: _____

FR: _____

RE: _____

DT: _____

SUMMARY OF PROJECT GOALS

_____

_____

_____

REPORT OF ACTION ON GOALS

_____

_____

_____

_____

_____

_____

_____

_____

RECOMMENDATIONS

_____

_____

_____

_____

PROJECT EVALUATION

Think of a project of which you have been a part and fill out this form based on your experience.

1. Describe the goal of the project. _____

_____

Was the goal met satisfactorily? (Rate the overall success of the project on a scale from 1 to 5.)

1	2	3	4	5
not met satisfactorily				met satisfactorily

2. Was the project an individual or a group effort? _____ individual _____ group
   (If the project was a group effort, rate the effectiveness of the group in each of the following areas on a scale from 1 to 5.)

   a. Cooperation among group leaders

1	2	3	4	5
not at all cooperative				very cooperative

   b. Leadership

1	2	3	4	5
not effective				very effective

   c. Division of tasks

1	2	3	4	5
unfair				fair

   d. Project organization

1	2	3	4	5
unorganized				organized

   (If the project was an individual effort, rate the effectiveness of the effort in each of the following areas on a scale from 1 to 5.)

   a. Effort

1	2	3	4	5
very little effort shown				much effort shown

   b. Creativity

1	2	3	4	5
very little creativity shown				much creativity shown

   c. Attention to goals

1	2	3	4	5
little attention to goals				much attention to goals

3. Rate the overall group or individual performance on a scale of 1 to 5 with regard to the criteria given above.

1	2	3	4	5
very poor performance				outstanding performance

(comments) _____

_____

_____

_____

_____

TECHNICAL WRITING

Technical writing refers to scientific or process oriented instructional writing that is of a technical or mechanical nature. Technical writing includes instruction manuals, such as computer software manuals, how-to instructional guides, and procedural memos. The step-by-step procedure "Research Strategies for the Learning Highway" on page 546 of your textbook is an example of technical writing.

   Think of a procedure, such as programming a VCR, with which you are familiar, and write a set of guidelines documenting the procedure. You may wish to refer to the Language Arts Survey 6.4, "Writing Step-by-Step Procedures."

_____

_____

_____

_____

_____

_____

_____

_____

_____

_____

_____

_____

_____

_____

_____

_____

_____

_____

_____

_____

_____

_____

_____

_____

_____

_____

Understanding Negotiation

Negotiation is an important skill in politics, in business, and in many other parts of life. Countries negotiate with one another about matters such as treaties and trade agreements. Businesses negotiate with one another and with individuals about such items as prices and contracts. Search in newspapers for examples of negotiation. Look in the world news sections of newspapers for political stories that deal with negotiation between countries. Look in the business news sections for stories dealing with negotiation between businesses. Look in the sports sections for stories dealing with negotiations between players and clubs or between clubs and government entities. Find at least three examples of negotiation. In each case, tell who is negotiating, what each side wants, and what the current status of the negotiation is.

Title of Newspaper Article: _____

Who is Negotiating: _____

What Each Side Wants: _____

_____

Current Status of the Negotiations: _____

_____

Title of Newspaper Article: _____

Who is Negotiating: _____

What Each Side Wants: _____

_____

Current Status of the Negotiations: _____

_____

Title of Newspaper Article: _____

Who is Negotiating: _____

What Each Side Wants: _____

_____

Current Status of the Negotiations: _____

_____

English in Marketing

PREPARING A MARKETING PLAN

Imagine that you work for a lawn service that is trying to expand its customer base. Design a marketing plan aimed at encouraging homeowners to use your service. Remember to give specific, detailed examples in your plan.

1. To whom will you market your lawn care services?

_____

_____

_____

2. How will you reach these people?

_____

_____

_____

3. What kind of advertising will you do?

_____

_____

_____

4. What community meetings will you attend to try to reach your market?

_____

_____

_____

5. What creative marketing ideas will you use?

_____

_____

_____

Other ideas:

_____

_____

_____

CREATIVE MARKETING

Use the following worksheet to create a marketing plan for a product or idea. Remember to focus on your product or idea and decide why it might appeal to people. Then think of a creative way in which to present it to people and encourage them to give it a chance.

Description of product or idea

_____

_____

_____

_____

_____

Positive features

_____

_____

_____

_____

_____

Questions people might ask

_____

_____

_____

_____

_____

Creative ideas for presenting product or idea

_____

_____

_____

_____

_____

_____

_____

CREATING A TOUR GUIDE

Imagine that you are a member of the Chamber of Commerce for your town or city. The state is producing a tour book, and you must submit a description of your area and its most interesting sights and features. Use the chart below to make a list of your town or city's libraries, schools, parks, playgrounds, public buildings, shops, landmarks, or any other interesting features. Then write a brief introduction to the area. Remember that your description should be useful to people who might be visiting, and it should also contain practical information for people who are moving to your area. If you live in a large city, you might want to limit the information you provide to places in your particular neighborhood or section of the city, but this is up to you. If you live in a very small town, you may include places that are outside your town but close by.

School(s) _____

Library(s) _____

Public park(s) _____

Playground(s) _____

Public office building(s) _____

Supermarket(s) _____

Shop(s)/store(s) _____

Landmark(s) _____

Other _____

Introduction to your town/city:

_____

_____

_____

_____

_____

_____

_____

_____

_____

_____

_____

_____

_____

_____

WRITING A CLASSIFIED ADVERTISEMENT

Imagine that you are trying to begin a pet-sitting service. On the lines below, write a classified ad for your local newspaper. Include the following information in the ad:

Pet-Sitting Service

Fees:

Availability:

Call: *[your name and number]*

Note: You may include any other information that you feel is necessary, but try to keep the number of words you use to a minimum.

_____

_____

_____

_____

_____

_____

_____

_____

_____

_____

_____

_____

_____

_____

_____

English in the Media

RESEARCHING LOCAL EVENTS AND MEETINGS

How would you begin to investigate what is happening in your community? Use the sheet below to record the information you find about the types of meetings and events that are being held this month in your city or town.

Local Newspaper:

_____

_____

_____

_____

Phone Directory:

_____

_____

_____

_____

Chamber of Commerce:

_____

_____

_____

_____

Word of Mouth:

_____

_____

_____

_____

Other Sources:

_____

_____

_____

_____

Developing a News Story

Imagine that you are a reporter for a newspaper assigned to cover the discovery of the drowned man found on the beach in "The Handsomest Drowned Man in the World," by Gabriel García Márquez on page 216 of your textbook. Write a newspaper article about the incident. Complete the following prewriting form before beginning your news story on the following page.

Write questions and answers to help you develop the lead, or introduction, to your news story:

Answers

Who _____ ? _____

What _____ ? _____

Where _____ ? _____

When _____ ? _____

Why _____ ? _____

Use the information above to write a **lead paragraph** for your story:

_____

_____

_____

_____

_____

Write a **headline** for your story. The headline should be a very short sentence without any articles (*a, an* or *the*).

_____

_____

_____

_____

Write the main idea that you will discuss in each of the paragraphs that follow your lead.

_____

_____

_____

_____

_____

_____

WRITING A NEWS STORY

_____

_____

_____

_____

_____

_____

_____

_____

_____

_____

_____

_____

_____

_____

_____

_____

_____

_____

_____

_____

_____

_____

_____

_____

_____

_____

_____

_____

_____

_____

_____

_____

PREPARING A NEWSPAPER ARTICLE

Imagine that you are a reporter asked to write a feature article about Monty Roberts and his methods of training horses (see the excerpt from *The Man Who Listens to Horses* on page 639 of your textbook). Since this is to be a factual article, try to remain objective and do not express any opinion or judgment about the events you are reporting. Include a headline and an idea for a picture with a caption.

PROOFREADING NEWS COPY

Newspaper columns must be proofread before they are printed and published. Imagine that you are a newspaper editor and that you have been assigned to proofread the following text. Using proofreader's marks, indicate how this passage should be corrected for errors in spelling, grammar, punctuation, and usage. See the Language Arts Survey 2.44 "Using Proofreader's Marks," for more information.

At a cermony meant to honor him Sammy Sosa insted made sure Roberto Clemente was not forgoten. Sosa told Puerto Rican senators who feted him with a specal meeting, Friday that a photograph he keeps of Clemente inspird him to his 61st and 62nd Homers, and later numbers 64 and 65. "I think I am the reincarnasion of Roberto Clemente" Sosa said.

The tribute touched Clemente's widow Vera. Her husband, a Hall of Famer who is, perhaps the greatest player Purto Rico has produced, died in a 1972 aircrash on his way deliver aid to earthqwake victims in Nicaragua. "He's not just a good baseball player, but a grate human being, "Vera Clemente said of Sosa in a voice chocked with emotion.

English Across the Curriculum

ENGLISH IN SCIENCE: SYLLOGISMS

A **syllogism** is a commonly used device of scientists testing their theories. It is a three-part argument consisting of a major premise, a minor premise, and a conclusion. The major premise offers a known generalization. The minor premise states a specific point. The conclusion logically follows from the first two parts. If it does not, it is a faulty conclusion.

EXAMPLES Correct:

All butterflies are insects.	(All A is B.)
This is a butterfly.	(This is A.)
It is an insect.	(Therefore it is a B.)

Faulty:

All birds can fly.	(All A is B.)
This butterfly can fly.	(This is B.)
This butterfly is a bird.	(Therefore it is A.)

A. Evaluating Syllogisms

Decide whether each syllogism is correct or faulty. Write a C next to each correct syllogism and an F next to each faulty one.

_____ 1. All U.S. citizens can vote at the age of 18.

Maria can vote.

Maria is 18.

_____ 2. All of my neighbors are homeowners.

The Abernathys are my neighbors.

The Abernathys are homeowners.

_____ 3. All of my classmates passed the math test.

Geoffrey passed the math test.

Geoffrey is my classmate.

B. Writing Syllogisms

In the space below, write two syllogisms of your own. Make sure that they are not faulty syllogisms.

_____

_____

_____

_____

_____

_____

_____

_____

ENGLISH IN SOCIAL STUDIES: GEOGRAPHY

In the excerpt "Long Drives on the Plains" on page 839 of your textbook, Ian Frazier describes a long journey across the plains. Refer to a road map of an area you would like to visit. Plot a cross-country journey of your choice, indicating the roads you would take. Draw a map of your route and write out directions in the space below.

ENGLISH IN SOCIAL STUDIES: HISTORY

Most history texts are organized in **chronological order**, showing sequences of events in the order in which they occurred. When you are researching a place or a series of events over a period of time, however, you may need to assemble the information in chronological order yourself or perhaps organize it in another way.

Read the excerpt from *Black Elk Speaks* on page 446 of your textbook. List the main events that Black Elk tells about in chronological order on the lines below.

_____

_____

_____

_____

_____

_____

_____

_____

_____

_____

_____

_____

_____

_____

_____

_____

_____

_____

_____

_____

_____

_____

_____

_____

_____

_____

_____

ENGLISH IN MATH: WRITING NUMBERS

In some cases, you may have to read or write numbers that are spelled out. Familiarizing yourself with the correct spellings and styles can help you with these tasks.

SOME NUMBER-WRITING TIPS

- Like numbers in a series or sentence should be consistently spelled out or written as numerals.
  She bought five apples, six pears, and twenty-four bananas.
- Write out numbers beginning sentences.
  Four hundred people attended the conference.
- Spell out simple fractions.
  More than two-thirds of the students wanted to eat outside.
- When writing out large numbers, use a comma where it appears in figure format.
  Exactly one million, four hundred seventy thousand, three hundred two letters arrived.
- Use the word *and* only where the decimal point appears in figure format.
  The stereo costs four hundred dollars and sixty-two cents.
- Hyphenate compound numbers from twenty-one to ninety-nine.
  The classroom counts were twenty-seven, thirty-one, and thirty-four.
- Do not hyphenate one hundred, two hundred, etc.
  One hundred sixty children went to the fair.

Writing Numbers

Write out the numbers in the following sentences.

1. Joshua bought 6 notebooks, 2 pens, 8 pencils, 2 erasers, and one 3-ring binder for his school supplies.

   _____

   _____

2. 643 students graduated from Springfield High School last spring.

   _____

   _____

3. More than 3/4 of the senior class students had plans to attend college or trade school.

   _____

   _____

4. The population of the metropolitan area has grown to 4,150,234.

   _____

   _____

5. The new computers will cost the school $1259.99 each.

   _____

   _____

ENGLISH IN HUMANITIES: COMPARING ART AND LITERATURE

Read the Art Note about the painting *Indian Spinning* by Diego Rivera on page 681 in your textbook. Write an essay describing how the woman in this painting is like or not like the narrator in the accompanying excerpt from "Straw into Gold: The Metamorphosis of the Everyday" by Sandra Cisneros.

_____

_____

_____

_____

_____

_____

_____

_____

_____

_____

_____

_____

_____

_____

_____

_____

_____

_____

_____

_____

_____

_____

_____

_____

_____

_____

_____

_____

_____

_____

_____

English in Your Personal Life

PRACTICAL WRITING

Writing is an efficient way to keep track of your daily and weekly plans and your long-term goals. Taking notes about things you hear on the radio, about conversations you take part in, and about ideas you have can help you remember concepts you want to research, books you want to read, or people you want to call. Making lists things you need to do can help you stay on top of your schedule. These types of writing can be kept in a journal or simple notebook. Writing notes to family members is a considerate way to make sure everyone in your home knows what your plans and needs are.

EXERCISE

Making Lists

1. Make a list of your plans for the coming weekend.

_____

_____

_____

_____

_____

_____

_____

_____

2. Make a list of your goals for the coming year.

_____

_____

_____

_____

_____

_____

_____

_____

_____

_____

_____

WRITING FOR PERSONAL EXPRESSION

A good way to get through a time in which you are afraid, sad, frustrated, or angry is to write. You may want to write about what is causing your bad feelings, or you may wish to write about happy things. Either way, you should simply write without any restrictions. In your own private writing, you can say anything you want to say, get your bad feelings off your chest, crumple up the paper and throw it away. Or you may choose to keep your writing and reflect back on it later. However you choose to approach this private writing, be honest with yourself and say what you want to say.

EXERCISE

Private Writing

Use the space below to write about something that may be bothering you. When you finish, tear up your paper and throw it away or fold it up and keep it in a safe, private place.

_____

_____

_____

_____

_____

_____

_____

_____

_____

_____

_____

_____

_____

_____

_____

_____

_____

_____

_____

_____

_____

CREATING A PERSONAL BUDGET

A budget is a plan for earning, spending, and saving money. Your income may come from allowance, gifts, babysitting, lawn work, and other sources. No matter how small your income and expenses, making a budget can help you to achieve your goals.

SAMPLE BUDGET

José wants a new video game system ($270), but his parents can't afford to buy it for him. José makes an allowance of $10 a week for doing chores around the house. He makes an additional $10 every other Saturday, doing yardwork for an elderly neighbor.

José's budget: Income per month: $60

        Expenses per month

                video games and snacks at the mall: $15

                movies: $5

                birthday and holiday gifts, miscellaneous: $10

        Savings per month: $30

If José saves $30 per month as his budget allows, he will be able to buy a video game system in about nine months.

EXERCISE

Creating a Budget

Use the space below to plan out your own budget.

_____

_____

_____

_____

_____

_____

_____

_____

_____

_____

_____

_____

_____

_____

_____

_____

_____

_____

Answer Key

Answer Key

6.1 FILLING OUT FORMS

A. Responses will vary. Some students may put "N.A." under e-mail. Hours and length of shift should be multiples of 2 or 4.
B. Responses will vary. Narrative parts of the application should be in complete sentences and well organized.

6.2 FOLLOWING DIRECTIONS

A. 1. To measure for you as you take the test
   2. That the partner needs a ruler to take the measurement
B. Responses will vary. Answers should be in the students' own words and reflect careful attention to the program and a basic understanding of the process described.

6.3 GIVING DIRECTIONS

A. Responses will vary. Answers should be accurate, clear, and easy to follow.
B. Responses will vary. A possible response is given.
   Sort clothes into white and colored articles. Measure and pour the detergent into the washing bin. Then choose the correct settings on the washer for your laundry load. Next start the machine. Wait about 15 seconds before putting in the clothes to make sure the detergent is dissolved or spread evenly around the bin. Then lay the clothes in loosely, filling the washer about 2/3 full. Close the lid. When the load is finished, take out the clothes immediately to avoid wrinkling. Then either hang up the clothes to dry or put them in the dryer. Take clothes out of the dryer as soon as the machine has finished its cycle.

6.4 WRITING A STEP-BY-STEP PROCEDURE

A. Responses will vary. A possible response is given.
   Show the application procedure for each cycling item one at a time. Display the supplies needed. Leave time for questions. Review the procedures quickly at the end of the presentation. Point out acceptable variations in the procedures. Warn children of things to watch out for, such as getting the tape stuck or tangled. Give tips on where to obtain the items.
B. Responses will vary. Answers should be accurate, clear, and easy to follow.

6.5 WRITING A BUSINESS LETTER

A. Responses will vary. Answers should reflect careful thought and preparation and show understanding or the elements of business letters as discussed in the activity introduction and on pages 1053-54 of the textbook.
B. Responses will vary. Answers should reflect careful thought and preparation and show understanding or the elements of business letters as discussed in the activity introduction and on page 1053-54 of the textbook.

6.6 WRITING A MEMO

A. Responses will vary. Memos should reflect careful thought and preparation, include all important information, and show understanding or the elements of memos as discussed in the activity introduction and on page 1055 of the textbook.
B. Responses will vary. Memos should reflect careful thought and preparation, include all important information, and show understanding or the elements of memos as discussed in the activity introduction and on page 1055 of the textbook.

6.7 Writing a Proposal

A. 1. The second one; it is more specific and focused.
2. Responses will vary. A possible response is given.
Both students and community members receive many benefits when students volunteer. Students provide valuable services, learn important skills for life and work, get to know different members of the community, and gain a better understanding of and sense of belonging to the community in which they live. The Volunteer Day project will help make students aware of the many opportunities that exist for volunteer service, as well as provide reasons why they should participate in a volunteer program.
3. Responses will vary. A possible response is given.
Organizations to be Represented, Publicity, Experienced Volunteers who Will Participate in the Program, Budget, Supplies Needed, Possible Timetable
B. Responses will vary. Proposals should reflect careful thought and preparation, include all important information, and show understanding or the elements of proposals as discussed in the activity introduction and on pages 1055-56 of the textbook.

6.8 Writing a Résumé

A. Responses will vary. Answers should reflect the information and sample résumé on page 1057 of the textbook.
B. Responses will vary. Qualifications that students mention should reflect those given in their résumé. Letters should be formal in tone, follow standard business-letter form, and include appropriate information that matches that supplied in the résumé.

6.9 Delivering a Press Release

A. Responses will vary. Releases should reflect careful thought and preparation, include all necessary information, and show understanding or the elements of press releases as discussed in the activity introduction and on page 1058 of the textbook.
B. Responses will vary. Releases should reflect careful thought and preparation, include all necessary information, and show understanding or the elements of press releases as discussed in the activity introduction and on page 1058 of the textbook, and of the play.

6.10 Writing a Public Service Announcement

A. Responses will vary. Students' PSAs should be accurate, complete, brief, and to the point and should cover likely questions about the event in brief form. They should also reflect understanding of the elements of a PSA as discussed on page 1058 of the textbook.
B. Responses will vary. Students' PSAs should be accurate, complete, brief, and to the point. They should also reflect understanding of the elements of a PSA as discussed on page 1058 of the textbook.

6.11 Displaying Effective Visual Information

A. Responses will vary. Ideas should be appropriate for the presentation subject and should be evaluated thoughtfully and accurately.
B. Responses will vary. The visual should be appropriate for the chosen subject and the format, should be functional and eye-catching, but not jarring, and text used should be readable, succinct, and logically arranged.

6.12 Working on a Team

A. Responses will vary. Possible responses are given.
1. I think we could use everyone's suggestions and make it funny, use music, and get some interesting props from the school.
2. Let's try not get away from our topic. I like Jordan's suggestions.

B. 1. Projects could range from anthologies and readings to written projects, artwork, and multimedia presentations.
2. Projects might be organized by theme or time period, by other criteria, or be focused on specific authors.
3. Particularly appropriate for the theme are poets Dickinson, Plath, Stafford, and Giovanni and prose writers Silko and Jen from Unit Seven of the text. Students may also include other authors not featured in the textbook.
4. Responses will vary.
5. Responses will vary.
6. Students should refer to some of the keys to effective team work summarized at the beginning of the exercise.

Supplemental Activity Worksheets

Proofreading News Copy

At a ceremony meant to honor him, Sammy Sosa instead made sure Roberto Clemente was not forgotten. Sosa told Puerto Rican senators who feted him with a special meeting Friday that a photograph he keeps of Clemente inspired him to his 61st and 62nd homers, and later numbers 64 and 65. "I think I am the reincarnation of Roberto Clemente," Sosa said.

The tribute touched Clemente's widow, Vera. Her husband, a Hall of Famer who is perhaps the greatest player Puerto Rico has produced, died in a 1972 air crash on his way to deliver aid to earthquake victims in Nicaragua. "He's not just a good baseball player, but a great human being," Vera Clemente said of Sosa in a voice choked with emotion.

English in Science: Syllogisms

1. F
2. C
3. F

English in Math: Writing Numbers

1. Joshua bought six notebooks, two pens, eight pencils, two erasers, and one three-ring binder for his school supplies.
2. Six hundred forty-three students graduated from Springfield High School last spring.
3. More than three-fourths of the senior class students had plans to attend college or trade school.
4. The population of the city has grown to four million, one hundred fifty thousand, two hundred thirty-four.
5. The new computers will cost the school one thousand two hundred fifty nine dollars and ninety-nine cents each.